Essential dictionary exercises

C000229034

compiled by
E.W. Hobson

Dictionary exercises to accompany
An essential dictionary

Schofield&Sims

© 2002 Schofield & Sims Ltd

978 07217 0940 6

First published 1980
This edition revised by Jo Phillips and Naomi Laredo
for SMALL PRINT
This edition first printed 2002
Fifth impression 2012

Cover design and illustration
by Curve Creative, Bradford

Printed in Great Britain
by Wyndeham Gait Ltd, Grimsby

Foreword

All the exercises in this book are based on words and definitions which are included in *An Essential Dictionary*. The exercises have been devised to encourage systematic, thorough and sensible use of a dictionary, leading to an extension and enrichment of vocabulary.

Exercise 1

Alphabetical order: first letter

The words in *An Essential Dictionary* are arranged in alphabetical order. First you will find all the words beginning with **A**, then all the words beginning with **B**, then those beginning with **C**, and so on right through the alphabet.

If we arrange the following words in alphabetical order:
diary   wood   team   model   zoo   absent   harbour   slice   last   police
we have:

absent   **di**ary   **h**arbour   **l**ast   **m**odel   **p**olice   **sl**ice   **t**eam   **w**ood   **z**oo

A   Now arrange these words in alphabetical order:
edge   talk   navy   zebra   mouse   accident
sleep   goat   uncle   jelly

B   Put these animals' names in alphabetical order:
wolf   elephant   lion   dog   antelope
squirrel   cat   mouse   rabbit   hare

C   Arrange these girls' names in alphabetical order:
Helen   Wendy   Alison   Mary   Susan   Emma

D   and these boys' names:
John   Roger   David   Barry   Trevor   Lee   Nigel

E   Now arrange the girls' and boys' names in C and D in one alphabetical list, beginning with:
Alison   Barry   . . . .

F   Here is a list of fruit. Arrange it in alphabetical order:
oranges   lemons   bananas   apples   pears
grapefruit   cherries   strawberries   raspberries

G   Arrange this list of sports in alphabetical order:
rowing   bowls   skating   football   tennis
yachting   wrestling   polo   golf

Exercise 2

Alphabetical order: second letter, third letter, fourth letter

In the dictionary, many words begin with the same letter. You can now try to put into alphabetical order words which begin with the same letter. For example, the names of these birds all begin with **s**:
swan   sandpiper   starling   skylark   snipe   sparrow

To list these birds in alphabetical order we need to look at the **second** letters and place them in order like this:
sandpiper   skylark   snipe   sparrow   starling   swan

A Now arrange this list of birds in alphabetical order using the second letter of each word:

puffin   peewit   partridge   pheasant   pigeon

When using a dictionary, we often have to find the word we need by looking at the **third** letter if the first two letters in each word are the same:

score   screen   school   scene   scare   science

So we place them in this order using the third letter:

scare   scene   school   science   score   screen

B Now place these words in alphabetical order using the third letter of each word:

scorch   screech   scholar   scent   scarf   scissors

C Now do the same with these words:

treacle   try   trot   trunk   trick   trap

D and these:

donkey   dozen   dock   dose   dog   doll

We sometimes have to look at the **fourth** letter to work out the alphabetical order:

Marcia   Margaret   Maria   Marjorie   Mary

E Use the fourth letter to place these words in alphabetical order:

prove   prowl   protect   proceed   profit   progress

Exercise 3

Alphabetical order
Place the following groups of words in alphabetical order.

A Using the first letters:

sign   injury   music   coin   rest   brown   eleven
leaf   actor   ostrich   zoo   dog   pound   giant

B Using the second letters:

thanks   team   toast   tyre   table   tractor   tide
tube   twig

C Using the third letters:

slide   slow   sly   slave   slush   sleep

D Using the fourth letters:

trap   travel   tray   transport   tramp   trawler   traffic
track   trade   trailer

E Sometimes we have to use more than the first four letters:

sleet   sleep   sleeve   sleek

Exercise 4

Now that you have had practice in arranging words in alphabetical order, here is a quick method of finding the page and word that you need.

On each page of the dictionary you will find the first and the last words of that page printed at the top. All the words on a page are in alphabetical order between these first and last words at the top of the page.

To find the word you need, first look at the two words shown at the top of the page.

Now use *An Essential Dictionary* to find these words. The number of dashes shows you the number of letters in the word. Copy and complete the sentences.

1 The **first** word beginning with **a** is _ _ _ _ _ _ _ .
   It is on page __ .

2 The first word beginning with **b** is _ _ _ _ .
   It is on page __ .

3 The first word beginning with **c** is _ _ _ _ _ _ _ .
   It is on page __ .

4 The first word beginning with **d** is _ _ _ .
   It is on page __ .

5 The first word beginning with **m** is _ _ _ _ _ _ _ _ .
   It is on page __ .

6 The first word beginning with **n** is _ _ _ .
   It is on page __ .

7 The first word beginning with **o** is _ _ _ .
   It is on page __ .

8 The first word beginning with **p** is _ _ _ _ _ .
   It is on page __ .

9 The **last** word beginning with **r** is _ _ _ .
   It is on page __ .

10 The last word beginning with **t** is _ _ _ _ .
    It is on page __ .

11 The first word beginning with **p** is on page __
    and the last word beginning with **p** is on page __ .

12 The first word beginning with **q** is on page __
    and the last word beginning with **q** is on page __ .

13 The first word beginning with **h** is _ _ _ _ _ .
    It is on page __ .

14 The last word beginning with **j** is _ _ _ _ _ _ _ _ .
    It is on page __ .

15 The first and last words beginning with **l** are _ _ _ _ _ and _ _ _ _ _ _ .

Exercise 5

The answers to these questions can all be found in the section of the dictionary where the words begin with the letters **b** or **c**.

Again, the number of dashes shows you the number of letters in each word. Start by finding the word which is printed in **bold** type. Then copy and complete the sentences. The first one is done for you.

1   A **bale** is a large **b u n d l e** .
2   A **belfry** is a bell- _ _ _ _ _ _ .
3   A **biped** is a two-footed _ _ _ _ _ _ .
4   A **bream** is a _ _ _ _ _ fish.
5   A **buoy** is a large, anchored _ _ _ _ _ .
6   A **cereal** is any grain used for _ _ _ _ .
7   A **churn** is used for making _ _ _ _ _ _ .
8   A **cobra** is a poisonous, hooded _ _ _ _ _ .
9   To **consent** means to _ _ _ _ _ _ .
10 **Custard** is a mixture of _ _ _ _ , eggs and sugar.

The answers to the next five questions can all be found in the section of the dictionary where the words begin with the letter **t**. Copy and complete the sentences.

11 A **talon** is the _ _ _ _ of a bird of prey.
12 A **tantrum** is a fit of bad _ _ _ _ _ _ .
13 A **tandem** is a _ _ _ _ _ _ _ for two riders.
14 A **tempest** is a violent _ _ _ _ _ .
15 **Thyme** is a sweet-smelling _ _ _ _ .

Exercise 6

The following words are in alphabetical order. Write down the word which is in **bold** type. Find its meaning and write the meaning alongside the word. The first one is done for you.

1   **abolish**   to do **a w a y** with
2   **buffalo**   a wild _ _
3   **coaster**   a _ _ _ _ _ _ trading between home ports
4   **dale**   a _ _ _ _ _ _
5   **exterior**   the _ _ _ _ _ _ _
6   **flaunt**   to show _ _ _

8

7	**gaudy**	bright and _ _ _ _ _
8	**howl**	a long _ _ _ _ _ _ _ cry
9	**invert**	to turn _ _ _ _ _ _ down
10	**jetty**	a landing _ _ _ _
11	**kale**	a _ _ _ _ _ vegetable
12	**lax**	_ _ _ _ _ _ _ _ ; slack
13	**mallet**	a _ _ _ _ _ _ hammer
14	**novel**	_ _ _ and original
15	**omit**	to _ _ _ _ _ out
16	**profile**	a _ _ _ _ view
17	**quit**	to go _ _ _ _
18	**recur**	to _ _ _ _ _ _ again
19	**shrub**	a small _ _ _ _
20	**talent**	a special _ _ _ _ _ or ability
21	**utilise**	to make _ _ _ of
22	**visible**	able to be _ _ _ _
23	**whey**	the watery part of _ _ _ _ milk
24	**xylophone**	a _ _ _ _ _ _ _ instrument
25	**yarn**	a _ _ _ _ or story
26	**zebra**	an _ _ _ _ _ _ _ wild animal

Exercise 7

An Essential Dictionary is a useful reference book. Look up the words in **bold** type and then write out and complete the sentences.

1 A **dinghy** is a small _ _ _ _ .
2 **Eaves** are the overhanging edges of a _ _ _ _ .
3 A **fife** is a small _ _ _ _ _ .
4 A **hasp** is a _ _ _ _ _ fastener for a door.
5 The soft lower part of the _ _ _ is known as the **lobe**.
6 A **molar** is a back _ _ _ _ _ .
7 An **otter** eats _ _ _ _ .
8 **Plastics** are made from _ _ _ _ _ _ _ _ _ .
9 **Vanilla** is obtained from a tropical _ _ _ _ _ _ .
10 A **whelk** is a small _ _ _ _ _ _ _ _ _ .

Exercise 8

Many words have more than one meaning or definition. Use *An Essential Dictionary* to look up the words in the first column below and you will find that each word has at least two correct definitions. Find these two correct definitions in the list in the second column. Write out the word with its meanings. The first one is done for you.

e.g. **1 limited**   restricted   narrow

1	**limited**	plenty	<u>restricted</u>	forbidden	boundary	<u>narrow</u>
2	**exceptional**	general	unusual	clever	abnormal	often
3	**suspicious**	careful	crafty	doubtful	accusing	distrustful
4	**rare**	novel	prolific	scarce	uncommon	sparse
5	**jovial**	shrill	merry	wise	cheerful	vicious
6	**data**	theme	time	facts	information	portion
7	**actual**	synthetic	existing	real	almost	extreme
8	**insolent**	empty	impudent	cheerful	rude	monotonous
9	**nourishment**	mixture	food	nutrition	stamina	ration
10	**superb**	nice	shrewd	splendid	reasonable	magnificent

Exercise 9

Occupations

You will find many occupations described in *An Essential Dictionary*.

A Write a short sentence, starting with the words given, describing the work done by each of the following. The first one is done for you.

1 A dentist is a person qualified and skilled in the care of teeth.

2 A plumber is a person who . . . .

3 A porter is a worker who carries . . . .

4 A journalist writes for . . . .

5 An engineer is a person who . . . .

6 A nurse is trained to . . . .

7 A butcher is a shopkeeper who . . . .

8 A judge is an official who . . . .

9 A greengrocer is a trader who . . . .

10 A reporter collects . . . .

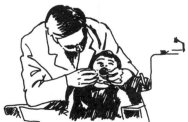

B Describe the following occupations:

1 an actor	**4** a producer	**7** a draughtsman	**10** a pharmacist
2 a doctor	**5** a lawyer	**8** a surgeon	
3 a pilot	**6** a playwright	**9** a financier	

Exercise 10

Geography

An Essential Dictionary is a useful reference book on many subjects. Use your dictionary to answer the following questions. From now on a line like this _____ tells you that a word is missing.

1 What is the difference between a **stalactite** and a **stalagmite**?

2 A **strait** is a narrow _____ of _____ connecting two seas.

3 What is meant by an **extinct** volcano?

4 Why is it dangerous to walk on **scree**?

5 Where do **rapids** occur in a river?

6 In what region of the world is the **Antarctic**?

7 What is meant by the **flora** of a region?

8 What is a **delta**?

9 **Irrigation** is a system of supplying _____ _____ with _____ to improve cultivation.

10 A **ravine** is a deep _____ _____ .

Exercise 11

Geography

Use *An Essential Dictionary* to answer these questions.

1 Where does **lichen** grow?

2 A **wold** is an area of open _____ _____ .

3 What does a **weir** control?

4 Is **Europe** the smallest or the largest continent?

5 Describe a region of **tundra**.

6 Is a **suburb** in the centre of a town or on the edge of it?

7 A **tarn** is a small, mountain _____ .

8 What is **lava** formed from?

9 A **loch** is a Scottish _____ .

10 What is the difference between **imports** and **exports**?

Exercise 12

Geography

Use *An Essential Dictionary* to answer these questions.

1 Is the water in a **lagoon** deep or shallow?
2 What would you find at an **oasis**?
3 What may be extracted from an **ore**?
4 A **plateau** is an area of _____ , _____ land.
5 What is a **tributary**?
6 A **dune** is a low hill of _____ .
7 What is **heath** land?
8 What is a **gully**?
9 **Shale** is a rock formed from _____ .
10 What is a **mere**?

Exercise 13

Complete the following sentences to show that you understand the meanings of the words printed in **bold** type.

1 There are _____ musicians in a **quintet**.
2 A **hovercraft** travels on a _____ of air.
3 **Lime** is used in making _____ .
4 A **predator** is an animal that hunts _____ .
5 A **fuselage** is the body of an _____ .

Exercise 14

What is kept or stored in:

1 a **silo**   3 a **menagerie**   5 a **cistern**?
2 a **kiosk**   4 a **paddock**

Exercise 15

What would you be an expert in if you were:

1 an **ornithologist**   3 an **astronomer**   5 a **sculptor**?
2 a **philatelist**   4 a **botanist**

Exercise 16

Complete and write out the following words and their meanings.

1 con _ _ er   *v.*   to defeat; to overcome.
2 dr _ _ ry   *adj.*   dull, boring, cheerless, gloomy.
3 em _ _ r   *n.*   a glowing or smouldering cinder.
4 grad _ _ nt   *n.*   amount of slope in a road, railway, etc.
5 leg _ _ le   *adj.*   clearly written; easy to read.

Exercise 17

Complete and write out the names of these birds and animals and draw a sketch of each one.

1 wr _ n   4 h _ r _   7 wea _ el   10 cu _ k _ _
2 t _ ger   5 bis _ n   8 ea _ l _
3 le _ p _ rd   6 fa _ con   9 ant _ lo _ _

Exercise 18

General knowledge

1 What is a **pseudonym**?
2 A **replica** is an _____ _____ .
3 What does a **glossary** contain?
4 Why are animals, people or ships sometimes placed in **quarantine**?
5 What is a **hangar** used for?

Exercise 19

There are many words that have opposite meanings. Look up each word from the first two columns in your dictionary and find a word from those in the box which has the opposite meaning. Write the opposites down in pairs.

Like this: **1**   north   south

1 north   6 friend
2 male   7 inferior
3 sharp   8 modern
4 minimum   9 answer
5 guilty   10 lower

enemy	question
innocent	maximum
raise	south
superior	female
ancient	blunt

Exercise 20

First find the meanings of the following words and then use them in sentences to show their meanings.

A		B	
1	rapid	**1**	majority
2	bough	**2**	enormous
3	data	**3**	utilise
4	talon	**4**	regatta
5	ravenous	**5**	propel

Exercise 21

An Essential Dictionary will tell you what you could expect to find in:

1 a vivarium **2** a museum **3** a holster **4** an eyrie **5** a warren

Exercise 22

Food and drink

An Essential Dictionary will give you information about food and drink and what they are made from. An **ingredient** is one of the materials or parts of a mixture.

Write down the main ingredients of:

A		B	
1	an omelette	**1**	jelly
2	wine	**2**	macaroni
3	soup	**3**	cider
4	marmalade	**4**	porridge
5	stew	**5**	bread

Exercise 23

Some words have similar pronunciation but are spelt differently and have differing meanings.

Choose the correct word and write out the completed sentences using *An Essential Dictionary* to help you.

1 The high tide covered the _____ . (beech, beach)
2 The house was for _____ . (sail, sale)
3 We climbed over the _____ into the field. (stile, style)
4 The plants were growing in _____ . (rows, rose)
5 The _____ team ran onto the field. (hole, whole)

Exercise 24

A **physician** is a person qualified to practise medicine.
Use *An Essential Dictionary* to describe the work of the following:

1 a tutor	**5** a manager	**9** an editor
2 a secretary	**6** an architect	**10** a steward
3 an Ombudsman	**7** a mason	
4 a treasurer	**8** an agent	

Exercise 25

Sports and games

An Essential Dictionary contains information on sports and games. Find the meanings of the words in **bold** type and then write an answer to each question.

1 What does an archer carry in a **quiver**?

2 The first **Olympic** Games were held at _____ , _____ .

3 **Judo** is a _____ form of wrestling.

4 A **stadium** is another name for a sports _____ .

5 A **trapeze** is a swinging bar used by _____ and _____ .

6 How many players take part in a game of **whist**?

7 There are _____ pieces in a set of **dominoes**.

8 What is the difference between an **amateur** and a **professional**?

9 How many pieces are there in a set of **draughts**?

10 What is a **sprint**?

Exercise 26

Weather and climate

The answers to these questions can all be found in *An Essential Dictionary*. Write out the answer in each case.

1 **Meteorology** is the study of the Earth's _____ and _____ .

2 What is a **temperate** climate?

3 **Nitrogen** makes up _____-_____ of the air.

4 An **observatory** is a building from which _____ study the _____ .

5 A **nimbus** cloud is a _____ cloud.

6 Why do you think early sailors disliked the **doldrums**?

7 A **drought** is a long period of _____ _____ .

8 What happens to the face of the sun or the moon during an **eclipse**?

9 Describe **cumulus** clouds.

10 What is **rainfall**?

Exercise 27

General knowledge

It is useful to increase your range of words. Look up the words in **bold** type, write down your answer and try to remember the meanings of these words.

1 Would a **taciturn** person have little or a lot to say?
2 **Protein**, an essential part of our diet, is found in _____ , _____ and _____ .
3 What is a **pretext**?
4 What could you buy in a **pharmacy**?
5 Who would wear a **mitre**?
6 Is a **pastel** colour light or dark?
7 What is **typhoid fever** caused by?
8 What is a **tiller** used for?
9 What was a Roman **gladiator** trained to do?
10 Where is the **façade** of a building?

Exercise 28

Detective work

The clues to the answers to these questions are the words in **bold** type.

1 What does the crime of **arson** involve?
2 What is a **felony**?
3 What does an **impostor** pretend to be?
4 A **witness** is a person who gives _____ in court.
5 A **writ** is a legal order requiring a person to _____ or _____ _____ something.
6 To commit **perjury** would be to give false _____ under _____ .
7 **Larceny** is the legal term for _____ or _____ .
8 What is the next rank above **inspector** in the police force?
9 What is a **forgery**?
10 A **clue** is a _____ or _____ that helps to solve a puzzle or mystery.

Exercise 29

Write out the following words and their meanings, putting in the missing letters. Start by referring to the first four letters which are given for each word.

1 subs _ dy: a financial grant or aid.
2 facs _ _ ile: an exact copy.

3 invo _ _ e: a list of goods supplied, with their prices and total cost; a bill.

4 stat _ _ _ ics: facts and figures collected, classified and arranged to give information.

5 mari _ _ _ e: having to do with the sea or ships.

Exercise 30

Calendar

These sentences refer to events or dates connected with the calendar. Write a sentence about each, first using *An Essential Dictionary* to obtain the information you need.

1 On what date would you expect to receive a **valentine**?
2 On what date are you likely to see a display of **pyrotechnics**?
3 When is **Hallowe'en**?
4 **Lent** is the _____ days before _____ .
5 An **annual** event happens _____ a _____ .
6 A **year** is the time taken by the _____ to travel once round the _____ .
7 What does the abbreviation **AD** represent?
8 What is an **anniversary**?
9 How many **quarterly** meetings are held in a year?

Exercise 31

Ships, sailing and the sea

This exercise is in four parts. Each question can be answered by referring to *An Essential Dictionary*. You could write out the answers or have a quiz with a friend.

A

1 Which is the **port** side and which is the **starboard** side of a ship?
2 Which is the **leeward** side of an island?
3 Write down two short descriptions of a **cruiser**.
4 What is a **purser** responsible for?
5 What does a **coxswain** do?
6 What is a **stowaway**?
7 A **pontoon** is a _____-_____ boat.
8 What is a **sextant** used for?
9 A **galley** was usually rowed by _____ .
10 How is a **turbine** engine operated?

B

1 What is a **kayak**?
2 How is **latitude** measured?
3 What was a **galleon**?
4 **Semaphore** is a code of signalling using movements of the _____ .
5 What would a **maritime** picture probably include?
6 In what year did the Spanish **Armada** attack England?
7 Why is **ballast** placed in an empty ship?
8 What is the difference between **flotsam** and **jetsam**?
9 What is a **ketch**?
10 A **flotilla** is a small _____ of ships.

C Use your dictionary to help you write descriptions of the following. The first one is done for you.

1 a dinghy: a small boat; an inflatable rubber boat
2 a freighter:
3 a regatta:
4 a yacht:
5 tidal:
6 a submarine:
7 a keel:
8 a launch:
9 a mooring:
10 naval:

D Write descriptions of:

1 a marine   5 a quay   9 a mariner
2 an anchor   6 a mermaid   10 a (ship's) mate
3 a punt   7 a tiller
4 a buoy   8 a sloop

Exercise 32

Write these sentences using the correct words in the spaces.

1 The sails were drawn _____ . (taught, taut)
2 Molten _____ poured from the volcano. (lava, larva)

3 The arrow on the weather _____ was pointing to the south. (vain, vane)

4 As the _____ rose, the anchor held the ship. (tide, tied)

5 A _____ is an inlet of the sea. (lock, loch)

From now on bold type is not used to emphasise words. You will need to read each question very carefully so that you can decide which important word in the sentence, or in the question, you need to refer to in your dictionary.

Exercise 33

Animals

Animals are very interesting to study. *An Essential Dictionary* will help you to learn something about them.

A

1 Name three types of reptile.

2 A nocturnal animal is active at _____ .

3 How does a python kill its prey?

4 Taxidermy is the art of . . . .

5 A gander is a _____ _____ .

6 A vixen is a female _____ .

7 Zoology is the scientific study of _____ .

8 Describe a yak.

9 Ermine is the white winter fur of a _____ .

10 For what is the whale hunted?

B

1 Which animal lives in a warren?

2 Which small rodent is similar to a vole?

3 A giraffe is an _____ animal with very long legs and neck.

4 Which animal family does the leopard belong to?

5 A reindeer lives in _____ _____ .

6 Give the names of three kinds of vermin?

7 On what does a mammal feed its young?

8 What would you expect to find in a lair?

9 A safari is an expedition to see or hunt _____ _____ .

10 A fawn is a young _____ .

Exercise 34

Maps

Here are five questions which will help you to understand maps.

1 What does the gradient of a road indicate?
2 What is the grid for on a map?
3 A kilometre is the equivalent of _____ metres.
4 What does a compass show?
5 From which place on the globe is longitude measured?

Exercise 35

General knowledge

Look up the clue words and then try the questions on a friend.

1 What is yoghurt made from?
2 A mule is a cross between a _____ and an _____ .
3 What does a joist support?
4 Give the names of two rodents.
5 How many arms has an octopus?

Exercise 36

Art

All the answers are in *An Essential Dictionary.*

1 Where would you expect to see a fresco?
2 A palette is a _____ on which an artist _____ _____ .
3 What colour is turquoise?
4 Is a profile a front view or a side view?
5 What is a mosaic made from?

Exercise 37

Revision

Put the following groups of words in alphabetical order:

1 zero echo salt wind oil mirror air radio light chalk
2 cylinder cube centre capacity chord cone circle
3 python pet psalm pitch pound puddle pray plumber path phantom
4 slim slink slit slide slip slight slice sling

Exercise 38

Farming

Use *An Essential Dictionary* to answer the following:

1 What is agriculture?
2 Kale is a green vegetable similar to a _____ .
3 What is land which is lying fallow?
4 What is a harrow used for?
5 What is arable land?
6 A cereal is a grain used as _____ .
7 Silage is made from green crops preserved in a _____ .
8 What is a fertiliser?
9 Why would a drought affect growing crops?
10 What does to thresh mean?

Exercise 39

Horses and riding

How much can you find out about horses and riding?

1 Where is a horse's fetlock?
2 A filly is a young _____ .
3 What is a halter used for?
4 How old is a yearling horse?
5 A foal is a young _____ .
6 What does the word equestrian mean?
7 What are stirrups?
8 A stallion is a _____ horse.
9 To canter is to ride at an _____ _____ .
10 How would you hobble a horse?

Exercise 40

Space flight and flying

Find out all you can about the following words, which are connected with space projects and flying. Write a sentence about each.

A

1 an orbit
2 aeronautics
3 a cosmonaut
4 a helicopter
5 an astronaut
6 a fuselage
7 a missile
8 a projectile
9 a laser
10 a capsule

B Now complete and write out these sentences:
1 A constellation is a _____ of _____ .
2 Radar is an electronic _____ device.
3 A satellite is a _____ sent travelling in orbit round a _____ .
4 A hangar is a building for housing _____ .
5 One type of projectile is known as a _____ .

Exercise 41

The following have all been famous ships of the Royal Navy. Write a motto for each. The first one is done for you.

A
1 Repulse: 'We Repel'
2 Formidable:
3 Valiant:
4 Glorious:
5 Resolution:

B
1 Illustrious:
2 Renown:
3 Victory:
4 Discovery:
5 Explorer:

Exercise 42

Weather

Here is an opportunity to find out more information about the weather.
1 A barometer measures _____ _____ .
2 An isobar is a line on a map connecting places that have the same _____ _____ .
3 Describe how a rainbow is formed.
4 What is inclement weather?
5 Where could you see the colours of the spectrum?

Exercise 43

Science

Write down your answers.
1 A dynamo is a machine for producing _____ .
2 What operates a pneumatic drill?
3 A hovercraft travels on a cushion of _____ .
4 What is adhesive used for?
5 What are plastics made from?

Exercise 44

What are the following used for?

For each of the following, write a sentence to describe what it is used for.

1 a thermostat	**5** a theodolite	**9** a videotape
2 a sextant	**6** an elevator	**10** a periscope
3 a solvent	**7** a protractor	
4 a rivet	**8** a pump	

Exercise 45

Increase your general knowledge by answering these questions.

1 How many sheets of paper are there in a quire?
2 What is the quotient of 2 and 10?
3 What is a refinery?
4 Write down the names of three quadrupeds.
5 What is a predator?

Exercise 46

Anagrams

An anagram is a word formed from the letters of another word. Clues in crosswords are often anagrams.

For example: HORSE : SHORE   LATE : TALE

Now do the following anagrams. The first two letters and the definition of each new word are given.

1 tide : ed _ _   to prepare material for printing, etc.
2 toast : st _ _ _   a small animal similar to the weasel
3 crate : tr _ _ _   to seek and find
4 plums : sl _ _ _   to collapse
5 rates : st _ _ _   to look continuously with a fixed gaze
6 charm : ma _ _ _   to walk with a regular step
7 peach : ch _ _ _   costing little
8 gates : st _ _ _   a raised platform
9 cheat : te _ _ _   to pass on knowledge or skill
10 laces : sc _ _ _   a series of graduated marks on a ruler, thermometer, map, etc.

Exercise 47

Ornithology is the study of birds. Write short descriptions of the following birds; they all appear in *An Essential Dictionary*. You could then find a book on birds, and illustrate each one.

A
1 wagtail
2 starling
3 tern
4 hawk
5 vulture

B
1 sparrow
2 finch
3 thrush
4 ostrich
5 owl

Exercise 48

Copy and complete the following. The first one is done for you.

Look in:	**To find:**
1 a dictionary	the meaning of a word
2 an album	
3 an atlas	
4 a register	
5 a calendar	
6 a diary	
7 a log	
8 a novel	
9 a biography	
10 a directory	

Exercise 49

Homes and buildings

An Essential Dictionary contains a description of each of these homes and buildings. With its help, answer the following questions:

A Who would live in:
1 a prison
2 a monastery
3 a convent
4 a palace
5 barracks?

B What would live in:
1 a stable
2 an eyrie
3 a hutch
4 a hive
5 an aviary?

C Write a sentence describing the purpose of these buildings:
  1 a studio   **3** an observatory   **5** a library
  2 a mint   **4** a surgery

Exercise 50
Food and drink

An Essential Dictionary contains words that you might read on menus or in recipes. Find out what you can about the following.

A What are these made from?
  1 custard   **3** chocolate   **5** sausage
  2 whisky   **4** pasta

B Write out the completed sentences:
  1 Gammon is smoked or _____ _____ .
  2 Venison is the flesh of a _____ .
  3 A salad is made from a mixture of _____ or _____ .
  4 A vegetarian is a person who eats no _____ .
  5 Cheese is made from _____ _____ .

C Complete or answer the following:
  1 Veal is the flesh of a _____ .
  2 Wine is usually made from the juice of _____ .
  3 Why is it essential to eat food containing vitamins?
  4 What is a flan?
  5 A recipe is a list of the _____ and _____ for preparing a dish.

D Make two lists, one of freshwater fish and the other of sea-fish:
  sole   pike   roach   cod   trout   perch
  bream   shark   plaice   haddock

E Copy and complete these sentences about vegetables:
  1 A carrot is an orange-coloured _____ vegetable.
  2 A cauliflower is a kind of flowering _____ .
  3 A leek is a vegetable of the _____ family.
  4 Beetroot is a vegetable with an edible _____ .
  5 An onion is an _____ bulb with a strong _____ .

25

Exercise 51

Holidays

The meanings of the words listed are not in the correct order. Write out each word with its correct meaning.

A

1	promenade:	a place where meals may be bought and eaten
2	motel:	the details or route of a journey
3	safari:	a place set aside for walking
4	restaurant:	an expedition to see or to hunt big game
5	itinerary:	a hotel for motorists

B

1	ramble:	the place to which a person or thing is going
2	haversack:	a pleasure trip; an outing
3	fare:	a walk for pleasure
4	excursion:	a canvas shoulder-bag for carrying food, clothing, etc.
5	destination:	the charge made for a journey

Exercise 52

Navy, army, air force

In films and books, on television and radio, you will meet many of the words in this exercise. Use *An Essential Dictionary* to help you to complete the following sentences and to answer the questions.

A

1 A battalion is part of a _____ of soldiers.

2 What does to navigate mean?

3 What does a pilot do?

4 A depot is a military _____ .

5 Promotion means a rise in _____ .

6 What is a recruit?

7 A major is an officer in rank between _____ and _____-_____ .

8 The Victoria Cross (VC) is awarded 'For Valour'. What is valour?

9 What is a periscope used for?

10 What is a sentinel?

B

1 What is a squadron?
2 An operation is a military _____ .
3 Why do you think a soldier in the artillery is known as a 'gunner'?
4 A missile is a weapon launched by a _____ .
5 A tank is an armoured fighting vehicle moving on _____ _____ .
6 Military means having to do with _____ or with _____ .
7 A marine is a _____ serving aboard a ship.
8 How is a glider different from an aeroplane?
9 What is an incendiary bomb?
10 What is meant by a ship being seaworthy?

C Look in the abbreviations at the back of *An Essential Dictionary* and then write down what the following represent.

1 Capt.	**3** GI	**5** HQ	**7** NATO	**9** RAF
2 Col.	**4** HMS	**6** Lieut.	**8** POW	**10** Sgt.

You will find the answers to Exercises 53 and 54 in *An Essential Dictionary*. Write down the questions and answers on History and Music and use them for a quiz in the class.

Exercise 53

History

1 When did the Saxons invade Britain?
2 Why were ramparts built round ancient towns?
3 What were Roman mosaic floors made from?
4 Which weapons have a hilt?
5 What does a visor protect?
6 Where did the Saxons come from?
7 What are fortifications?
8 Describe Gothic architecture.
9 Give another name for the Neolithic Age.
10 What is a manuscript?

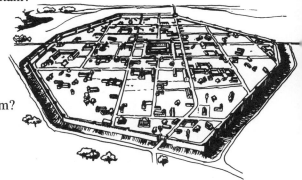

Exercise 54
Music

1 A viola is a stringed instrument like a large _____ .
2 Tenor describes a male voice between _____ and _____ .
3 A melody is an arrangement of _____ _____ .
4 An octave is a span of _____ _____ _____ .
5 A quintet is a group of _____ _____ or _____ .
6 When is an overture performed?
7 An oboe is a _____-_____ instrument.
8 A lament is a _____ song.
9 Explain how a xylophone works.
10 A duet is music performed by two _____ or _____ .

A dictionary is sometimes used for speedy reference. Time yourself for each of the next two exercises. Write down the answers. You must be accurate as well as speedy.

Exercise 55
What would you find by reading:

1 an obituary
2 an encyclopedia
3 a (musical) score
4 a script

5 the Koran
6 a log
7 a manifesto
8 an epilogue

9 an epitaph
10 a will?

Exercise 56
Sport

1 In ball games, what is a volley?
2 Give another name for skittles.
3 What sport would take place on a rink?
4 What is another name for a sledge?
5 How many players are there in a hockey team?
6 What is a novice player?
7 In sport, what is a penalty?
8 Who would use a trapeze?
9 In what games is a cue used?
10 What is the meaning of versus?

Exercise 57

Sometimes words sound the same but have different spellings and meanings. Look up the meanings of the words in brackets. Then write out each sentence and include the correct word.

A

1 The bride walked down the _____ . (isle, aisle)
2 William the First came to the _____ in 1066. (thrown, throne)
3 The water _____ burst and caused a flood. (main, mane)
4 The raft was carried away by the swiftly flowing _____ . (currant, current)
5 _____ is made from the juices of grapes. (Wine, Whine)

B

1 A gold _____ was awarded to the champion. (medal, meddle)
2 Silently the cat stalked its _____ . (pray, prey)
3 There is no need to _____ so rudely. (stare, stair)
4 The fishing-line suddenly pulled _____ . (taught, taut)
5 _____ me outside the supermarket. (Meat, Meet)

Exercise 58

Acting

A Write out the definitions in a column and then write the correct word from the following list alongside each definition.

character   playwright   producer   pantomime   comedy

1 an amusing play
2 a person who writes plays
3 a person in a play
4 a Christmas entertainment based on a fairy story
5 the person supervising the presentation of a stage, film or television performance

B Do the same with the following:

script   rehearsal   tragedy   stage   drama

1 a practice in preparation for a performance
2 a play with an unhappy ending
3 the text of a film, play, radio or television programme
4 a raised platform
5 a play for television, theatre or radio

Exercise 59

People

Answer the following:

A

1 Is your paternal grandfather your mother's father or your father's father?
2 Write a sentence to describe the work of a draughtsman.
3 What is a pacifist opposed to?
4 Is a sentinel similar to a sentry?
5 How does a vagrant spend his or her life?

B

1 What does a hermit choose to do?
2 Does a tenant own the house he or she occupies?
3 What is a warden often in charge of?
4 Write a sentence to describe the work of a reporter.
5 What is a delegate appointed to do?

Exercise 60

This is an exercise which includes several uses of the dictionary that you have tried earlier.

Write out these sentences using the correct words:

1 The bride wore a white _____ . (vale, veil)
2 This machine is _____ in England. (made, maid)
3 The breaking of the high jump record was a great _____ . (feat, feet)

Complete these sentences:

4 Latin was the language of the _____ _____ .
5 Neolithic man lived in the _____ _____ _____ .
6 Macaroni is made from _____ _____ .

You will find these abbreviations in the appendix of *An Essential Dictionary*. What do they represent?

7 anon.   misc.   ref.   tel.   max.

Answer these questions:

8 How many pairs of wings has a monoplane?
9 How many prongs has a trident?
10 What would you get if you received a legacy?

Exercise 61

What are the following?

1 a title   3 a preface   5 a prologue
2 a narrative   4 a questionnaire

Exercise 62

This exercise will give you practice in dealing with words that have similar beginnings. Complete these words. Write them down with their definition alongside.

1 ant _ _ _ tic: the south polar region
2 ant _ _ ue: old and rare
3 ant _ _ r: a branch of a stag's horn
4 dis _ _ nd: to break up; to disperse
5 dis _ _ bark: to put or go ashore from a ship
6 dis _ _ _ est: not honest
7 dis _ _ ey: to refuse or ignore an instruction or order
8 en _ _ ge: to make angry
9 en _ _ ch: to make rich
10 en _ _ oach: to trespass

Exercise 63

Another mixed exercise using the dictionary in ways you have done before.

A Write sentences which include these words:

1 glorious   2 gaunt   3 enormous   4 thrive   5 pennant

B See what you can find about:

1 a beret   2 a helmet   3 a veil   4 a fez   5 a turban

C Answer these questions:

1 What is a flue?
2 What does a weir control?
3 What does a thermostat control?
4 What does an aqueduct carry?
5 What does a valve control?

D What do these abbreviations represent?

1 i.e.   2 para.   3 o.n.o.   4 p.a.   5 e.g.

Exercise 64

A **Sub** at the beginning of a word means 'under'. Why do these words begin with **sub**? Write out each word with your explanation alongside.

subway   submarine   subterranean

B Complete these words:

1 quad _ _ ple: an amount four times as great
2 sub _ _ de: to sink or to settle down
3 nov _ _ ty: a new or unusual item
4 pre _ _ ct: to foretell or to forecast
5 pre _ _ se: clear in meaning

C Copy and complete these sentences:

1 A recluse is a person who lives . . . .
2 A novice is a _____ or _____ .
3 A vandal is a person who deliberately . . . .
4 A fugitive is a person who . . . .
5 An employee is a person who . . . .

Now that you have had a lot of practice in using *An Essential Dictionary*, you should be used both to finding out how to spell words and to finding the meanings of words.

You can now try the ten tests that follow in Exercises 65 to 74.
Remember
1 Read the question carefully.
2 Take care to find the correct word.
3 Answer with a sentence where necessary.
4 Do not rush. These are **not** speed tests.
5 You must be accurate.

Exercise 65

Test yourself 1

1 A deft movement would be _____ and _____ .
2 Would a fictitious name be real or false?
3 Is nutritious food good for you?
4 A provocative remark could be _____ and annoying.
5 Would porous material hold water?

6 What is meant by a temperate climate?
7 Give another name for a rowan tree.
8 Who founded the Wesleyan Church?
9 Would it be safe to step into tepid water?
10 A ha _ _ is a bird of prey.

Exercise 66

Test yourself 2

1 Which city is the metropolis of England?
2 Greeks come from _____ .
3 Bellows are used for . . . .
4 Rancid butter tastes or smells _____ or _____ .
5 What is a parallelogram?
6 Who might use a pair of forceps?
7 Find a word that means the same as ruse.
8 To om _ _ is to leave out.
9 Where does lichen grow?
10 PTO on a page means _____ _____ _____ .

Exercise 67

Test yourself 3

1 If you were given an option, what would you have?
2 A gosling is a young _____ .
3 Is an adder a poisonous snake?
4 What grows in a coppice?
5 Put these words in alphabetical order:
   rhyme   red   road   rat   rye   rice   rubber
6 From what does the eiderdown get its name?
7 The Swiss come from _____ .
8 How would you describe a timorous person?
9 A research worker seeks to discover new _____ .
10 What is the EU?

Exercise 68

Test yourself 4
Copy and complete these sentences using the words
from the box.

1   A _____ is a group of sheep or birds.
2   A _____ is a large bird with webbed feet.
3   A _____ is a building in which horses are kept.
4   A _____ is a long-handled spoon.
5   A _____ is a Jewish religious leader.
6   _____ is a sweet-smelling herb used in cooking.
7   A _____ is a small poisonous snake.
8   A _____ is a small, rocky hill.
9   A _____ is a metal fastener for a door or lid.
10 A _____ is a spear or hook for landing large fish.

Thyme
hasp
gaff
goose
tor
flock
stable
rabbi
ladle
viper

Exercise 69

Test yourself 5
Copy and complete these sentences using the words
from the box.

1   Some animals _____ during the winter.
2   A _____ is a person who has just joined the army.
3   A _____ writes articles for newspapers and
magazines.
4   A _____ is a stand with three legs.
5   The backbone is also known as the _____ .
6   Short stalks of corn left in the ground after reaping
are known as _____ .
7   A _____ is used to keep a daily record of events.
8   A _____ is a strong sinew connecting a bone
to a muscle.
9   An _____ is a part of an atom.
10 _____ is a bright red colour.

tripod
spine
electron
Vermilion
diary
hibernate
tendon
stubble
recruit
journalist

Exercise 70

Test yourself 6

Where would the following probably live?

Copy the list and then write the correct answers alongside, using the phrases from the box.

1	mariner	in the sea
2	gipsy	near a river
3	soldier	on a ship
4	monk	in a tree
5	newt	in a convent
6	haddock	in a caravan
7	nun	in a vicarage
8	hippopotamus	in barracks
9	vicar	in water, but can survive on land
10	squirrel	in a monastery

Exercise 71

Test yourself 7

1 Is a docile animal usually obedient?

2 To end_ _ _ _ means to approve or agree to something.

3 A lethal dose of poison would cause _____ .

4 On what does a mammal feed its young?

5 Evasive answers can be mis _ _ _ _ ing.

6 What does an otter feed on?

7 Would you be likely to catch a disease to which you are immune?

8 Is a molar tooth at the back or the front of the mouth?

9 The larynx contains the _____ _____ .

10 What is a mercenary?

Exercise 72

Test yourself 8

1 A penguin is a bird that can _____ but cannot _____ .

2 What is a spoor?

3 What is a dilapidated building?

4 Can ships sail up a navigable river?

5 The yolk is the _____ part of an egg.
6 A maple tree is similar to a _____ tree.
7 What is a labyrinth?
8 Is legible writing easy to read?
9 What is a proverb?
10 A magistrate is also known as a . . . .

Exercise 73

Test yourself 9

1 What is a female tailor called?
2 A currant is a dried _____ .
3 What is a remnant of cloth?
4 A sequence is the arrangement in which . . . .
5 Would you hear an ultrasonic sound?
6 How is a verbatim report written down?
7 A ballad is a simple song or poem telling a _____ .
8 A conifer is a tree that bears _____ .
9 Which part of a shoe is the welt?
10 What is a retriever dog trained to do?

Exercise 74

Test yourself 10

1 What is a regulation?
2 A scarp is the _____ _____ of a hill.
3 A centenary is the _____ anniversary.
4 What would you find round the sides of a tambourine?
5 The reflecting surface of a convex mirror curves _____ .
6 An anagram is a word formed from . . . .
7 What makes a tarpaulin watertight?
8 A botanist is a person who studies _____ .
9 A rout is a complete _____ .
10 What is a tracery?

ANSWERS

Exercise 1

A	B	C	D	E	F	G
accident	antelope	Alison	Barry	Alison	apples	bowls
edge	cat	Emma	David	Barry	bananas	football
goat	dog	Helen	John	David	cherries	golf
jelly	elephant	Mary	Lee	Emma	grapefruit	polo
mouse	hare	Susan	Nigel	Helen	lemons	rowing
navy	lion	Wendy	Roger	John	oranges	skating
sleep	mouse		Trevor	Lee	pears	tennis
talk	rabbit			Mary	raspberries	wrestling
uncle	squirrel			Nigel	strawberries	yachting
zebra	wolf			Roger		
				Susan		
				Trevor		
				Wendy		

Exercise 2

A	B	C	D	E
partridge	scarf	trap	dock	proceed
peewit	scent	treacle	dog	profit
pheasant	scholar	trick	doll	progress
pigeon	scissors	trot	donkey	protect
puffin	scorch	trunk	dose	prove
	screech	try	dozen	prowl

Exercise 3

A	B	C	D	E
actor	table	slave	track	sleek
brown	team	sleep	trade	sleep
coin	thanks	slide	traffic	sleet
dog	tide	slow	trailer	sleeve
eleven	toast	slush	tramp	
giant	tractor	sly	transport	
injury	tube		trap	
leaf	twig		travel	
music	tyre		trawler	
ostrich			tray	
pound				
rest				
sign				
zoo				

Exercise 4

1 abandon 9	**4** dab 38	**7** oak 102	**10** tyre 164	**13** habit 69
2 baby 15	**5** macaroni 90	**8** pace 105	**11** 105 120	**14** juvenile 84
3 cabaret 23	**6** nag 99	**9** rye 131	**12** 120 121	**15** label lyric

Exercise 5

1 bundle	**4** river	**7** butter	**10** milk	**13** bicycle
2 tower	**5** float	**8** snake	**11** claw	**14** storm
3 animal	**6** food	**9** agree	**12** temper	**15** herb

ANSWERS

Exercise 6

1	away	7	showy	12	careless	17	away	22	seen
2	ox	8	wailing	13	wooden	18	happen	23	sour
3	vessel	9	upside	14	new	19	bush	24	musical
4	valley	10	pier	15	leave	20	skill	25	tale
5	outside	11	green	16	side	21	use	26	African
6	mare							

Exercise 7

1	boat	3	flute	5	ear	7	fish	9	plant
2	roof	4	metal	6	tooth	8	chemicals	10	shellfish

Exercise 8

1	restricted	narrow	6	facts	information
2	unusual	abnormal	7	existing	real
3	doubtful	distrustful	8	impudent	rude
4	scarce	uncommon	9	food	nutrition
5	merry	cheerful	10	splendid	magnificent

Exercise 9

A

1 A dentist is a person qualified and skilled in the care of teeth.
2 A plumber is a person who installs and repairs water-pipes, taps, etc.
3 A porter is a worker who carries luggage or loads.
4 A journalist writes for a newspaper, magazine or journal.
5 An engineer is a person who designs, makes or operates machinery.
6 A nurse is trained to look after sick or injured people.
7 A butcher is a shopkeeper who sells meat.
8 A judge is an official who tries accused persons in a court of law.
9 A greengrocer is a trader who sells fresh fruit and vegetables.
10 A reporter collects news and information for a newspaper, radio or television.

B

1	an actor:	a player on stage, radio, television, or in films
2	a doctor:	a person qualified to treat the sick and injured
3	a pilot:	a person who controls an aircraft during flight; a person who steers ships in and out of harbour
4	a producer:	a person who supervises stage, film or television performances
5	a lawyer:	a person skilled in law or legal work
6	a playwright:	a person who writes plays
7	a draughtsman:	a person who designs and draws plans
8	a surgeon:	a doctor who performs operations
9	a financier:	a person who arranges finance
10	a pharmacist:	a person qualified to prepare medicines

ANSWERS

Exercise 10

1 A stalactite hangs from the cave roof. A stalagmite rises from the cave floor.
2 channel, water
3 a volcano which is no longer active
4 There is a danger of slipping on the loose, small stones.
5 where water flows rapidly over rocks
6 in the south polar region
7 the plants of a region
8 the triangle of land formed by the mouths of a large river
9 dry land, water
10 narrow valley

Exercise 11

1 on rocks and trees
2 undulating country
3 the flow of water in a river
4 the smallest
5 a vast, treeless plain with arctic climate and vegetation
6 on the edge
7 lake
8 the molten matter that flows from a volcano
9 lake
10 Imports are goods brought into a country from abroad. Exports are goods sent abroad.

Exercise 12

1 shallow
2 water
3 metal
4 high, level
5 a stream or river flowing into another
6 sand
7 uncultivated land covered with heather or scrub
8 a channel worn by running water
9 clay
10 a pond or lake

Exercise 13

1 five   2 cushion   3 cement   4 prey   5 aircraft

Exercise 14

1 grains or crops   3 wild animals   5 water
2 newspapers or   4 horses
   refreshments or
   a telephone

ANSWERS

Exercise 15

1 birds
2 postage stamps
3 stars and their movements
4 plants
5 carving and modelling

Exercise 16

1 conquer   **2** dreary   **3** ember   **4** gradient   **5** legible

Exercise 17

1 wren
2 tiger
3 leopard
4 hare
5 bison
6 falcon
7 weasel
8 eagle
9 antelope
10 cuckoo

Exercise 18

1 an assumed name
2 exact copy
3 a list of words and their meanings
4 to prevent the spread of disease
5 housing aircraft

Exercise 19

1 north   south
2 male   female
3 sharp   blunt
4 minimum   maximum
5 guilty   innocent
6 friend   enemy
7 inferior   superior
8 modern   ancient
9 answer   question
10 lower   raise

Exercise 20

The sentences should show the following meanings:

A   *Meaning*
1 rapid: quick; speedy
2 bough: a branch of a tree
3 data: facts; information
4 talon: the claw of a bird of prey
5 ravenous: very hungry

B   *Meaning*
1 majority: the greater number; the larger part
2 enormous: very large; immense; huge
3 utilise: to make use of
4 regatta: a race meeting for boats and yachts
5 propel: to drive on or push forward

Exercise 21

1 animals in their natural state
2 old, interesting and valuable objects
3 a pistol
4 an eagle or other bird of prey
5 rabbits

ANSWERS

Exercise 22

A

1 beaten eggs, and often herbs, ham, cheese, etc.
2 the juice of grapes or other fruits
3 liquid, meat, vegetables, etc.
4 oranges, lemons or grapefruit
5 meat and vegetables

B

1 gelatine
2 flour paste
3 apple juice
4 oatmeal, with water or milk
5 flour and water

Exercise 23

1 beach   2 sale   3 stile   4 rows   5 whole

Exercise 24

1 A tutor teaches or instructs.
2 A secretary deals with correspondence, records, arrangements, etc.
3 An Ombudsman considers the grievances of individuals.
4 A treasurer is responsible for the funds and accounts of a club, society or business.
5 A manager is in charge of a business, hotel or shop.
6 An architect plans and designs buildings.
7 A mason works with stone.
8 An agent is a person who acts for another; a representative.
9 An editor chooses what is to be included in a book, newspaper, film, etc.
  OR
  An editor prepares the work of others for publication.
10 A steward caters for a club or college, or manages an estate or race-course, or is an attendant on a ship or aircraft.

Exercise 25

1 arrows
2 Olympia, Greece
3 Japanese
4 arena
5 gymnasts, acrobats
6 four
7 28
8 a professional is paid
9 24
10 a short, fast run or race

Exercise 26

1 weather, atmosphere
2 a moderate climate; one which is neither very hot nor very cold
3 four-fifths
4 astronomers, heavens
5 storm
6 there was no wind to fill their ships' sails
7 dry weather
8 it is darkened
9 white, woolly clouds heaped one above the other
10 the amount of rain that falls in a given time at a particular place

ANSWERS

Exercise 27

1 a little
2 eggs, meat, milk
3 an excuse
4 medicines
5 a bishop
6 light
7 by germs in contaminated water or food
8 to turn the rudder of a small boat
9 to fight in an arena with other men or with wild animals
10 at the front of a building

Exercise 28

1 setting property on fire deliberately
2 a serious crime
3 somebody else
4 evidence
5 do, stop doing
6 evidence, oath
7 theft, pilfering
8 superintendent
9 a copy made with intent to deceive
10 hint, idea

Exercise 29

1 subsidy   2 facsimile   3 invoice   4 statistics   5 maritime

Exercise 30

1 14th February
2 5th November
3 31st October, the evening before All Saints' Day
4 forty, Easter
5 once, year
6 Earth, sun
7 Anno Domini (Latin): in the year of our Lord
8 the date of an annual event or celebration
9 four

Exercise 31

A

1 port is the left side, starboard is the right side
2 the sheltered side
3 a fast warship; a small boat for pleasure cruising

ANSWERS

4 accounts and money on board a ship
5 he/she steers a boat
6 a person who hides in a ship or aircraft to avoid paying the fare
7 flat-bottomed
8 to measure the angles between two distant objects when navigating
9 slaves
10 by a jet of gas, steam or air

B

1 an Eskimo canoe
2 by measuring the distance north or south of the equator in degrees
3 a large Spanish sailing-ship
4 arms
5 the sea and ships
6 1588
7 to steady it
8 Flotsam is cargo or wreckage found floating on the sea. Jetsam is goods thrown overboard from a ship and then washed ashore.
9 a two-masted sailing-boat
10 fleet

C

1 a dinghy: a small boat; an inflatable rubber boat
2 a freighter: a cargo ship (also an aircraft, a lorry or a train)
3 a regatta: a race meeting for boats and yachts
4 a yacht: a sailing-boat built for racing or cruising
5 tidal: affected by or concerned with the tides
6 a submarine: a ship which can travel under water
7 a keel: the beam on which the framework of a ship is built
8 a launch: a motor boat
9 a mooring: a place to moor a boat
10 naval: to do with the navy

D

1 a marine: a soldier serving aboard a ship
2 an anchor: a heavy metal hook which grips the sea-bed and holds a ship at its moorings
3 a punt: a flat-bottomed boat propelled by a long pole
4 a buoy: a large, anchored float to guide ships
5 a quay: a place for the loading and unloading of ships
6 a mermaid: an imaginary creature with the body of a woman and the tail of a fish
7 a tiller: a lever used to turn the rudder of small boats
8 a sloop: a one-masted sailing-ship
9 a mariner: a sailor; a seaman
10 a (ship's) mate: a ship's officer who is second in command

ANSWERS

Exercise 32

1 taut   **2** lava   **3** vane   **4** tide   **5** loch

Exercise 33

A

1 snake, lizard, crocodile
2 night
3 by coiling round its prey and crushing it
4 stuffing the skins of animals, birds and fish to make them look life-like
5 male goose
6 fox
7 animals
8 a long-haired, humped ox
9 stoat
10 for its oil and whalebone

B

1 a rabbit
2 a mouse
3 African
4 the cat family
5 cold regions
6 (three of) mice, rats, fleas, lice
7 on its own milk
8 a wild animal
9 big game
10 deer

Exercise 34

1 the amount of slope in a road
2 it forms the basis for map references
3 1000
4 magnetic north
5 Greenwich

Exercise 35

1 fermented milk
2 horse, ass
3 a floor or ceiling
4 rat, squirrel
5 eight

ANSWERS

Exercise 36
1 painted on a wall
2 board, mixes colours
3 greenish-blue
4 a side view
5 small pieces of glass or stone

Exercise 37
1 air   chalk   echo   light   mirror   oil   radio   salt   wind   zero
2 capacity   centre   chord   circle   cone   cube   cylinder
3 path   pet   phantom   pitch   plumber   pound   pray   psalm   puddle   python
4 slice   slide   slight   slim   sling   slink   slip   slit

Exercise 38
1 the cultivation of the land
2 cabbage
3 it is ploughed but unplanted
4 breaking up ploughed land
5 land fit for ploughing and growing crops
6 food
7 silo
8 manure or chemicals put into the soil to make it more fertile
9 growing crops need water
10 to separate the grain from the husks in ears of corn

Exercise 39
1 on the back of the leg, just above the hoof
2 mare
3 leading horses
4 one year old
5 horse
6 (*adj.*) having to do with horses; (*n.*) a person riding on horseback
7 supports hanging from a saddle, for the horse-rider's feet
8 male
9 easy gallop
10 by tying a rope between two of its legs

ANSWERS

Exercise 40

A

1	An orbit is	the path in which a planet, satellite or spacecraft moves round another body.
2	Aeronautics is	the science of navigation in the air.
3	A cosmonaut is	a person who travels in space; an astronaut.
4	A helicopter is	an aircraft able to take off and land vertically and to hover.
5	An astronaut is	a person who travels in space; a cosmonaut.
6	A fuselage is	the body of an aircraft.
7	A missile is	a weapon thrown, fired or launched by a rocket.
8	A projectile is	something thrown or shot through the air; a missile.
9	A laser is	a device which strengthens an input of light, producing an extremely narrow and intense beam.
10	A capsule is	part of a spacecraft.

B

1 group, stars
2 navigational
3 spacecraft, planet
4 aircraft
5 missile

Exercise 41

A

1	Repulse:	'We Repel'
2	Formidable:	A motto using: to be dreaded; hard to overcome
3	Valiant:	A motto using: brave; courageous
4	Glorious:	A motto using: splendid; magnificent; famous; renowned
5	Resolution:	A motto using: firmness; determination

B

1	Illustrious:	A motto using: famous; celebrated; distinguished
2	Renown:	A motto using: fame; glory; honour
3	Victory:	A motto using: success in a contest or battle
4	Discovery:	A motto using: the act of discovering
5	Explorer:	A motto using: something that makes a journey of exploration; something that makes a search

Exercise 42

1 air pressure
2 atmospheric pressure
3 it is formed by the sun shining through raindrops
4 severe weather
5 in a rainbow or through a glass prism

ANSWERS

Exercise 43
1 electricity
2 compressed air
3 air
4 for sticking things together
5 chemicals

Exercise 44
1 A thermostat is used for controlling temperature.
2 A sextant is used in navigating and surveying to measure the angle between two distant objects.
3 A solvent is used for dissolving other substances.
4 A rivet is used for fastening metal plates together.
5 A theodolite is used in surveying to measure horizontal and vertical angles.
6 An elevator is used to raise things to a higher level.
7 A protractor is used for measuring angles.
8 A pump is used for pumping air or liquids through a pipe.
9 A videotape is used to record television pictures.
10 A periscope is used for viewing objects above the surface or above eye-level.

Exercise 45
1 25
2 5
3 a place where materials are purified
4 cow, horse, dog, etc.
5 an animal that hunts prey

Exercise 46
1 edit
2 stoat
3 trace
4 slump
5 stare
6 march
7 cheap
8 stage
9 teach
10 scale

Exercise 47
A
1 wagtail: a small bird with a long tail
2 starling: a common bird with glossy bluish-black feathers
3 tern: a small sea-bird with pointed wings and forked tail
4 hawk: a bird of prey in the eagle family
5 vulture: a large, bald-headed bird of prey that feeds on decaying flesh

B
1 sparrow: a small, common, brownish bird which nests in hedges or houses
2 finch: one of various small song-birds
3 thrush: a song-bird with a brown back and speckled breast
4 ostrich: a large, fast-running African bird that cannot fly
5 owl: a night-flying bird of prey

ANSWERS

Exercise 48

	Look in:	To find:
1	a dictionary	the meaning of a word
2	an album	pictures, stamps, etc.
3	an atlas	maps
4	a register	official records
5	a calendar	days, weeks, months, dates
6	a diary	a daily record of events
7	a log	a record of an aircraft's flight or a ship's voyage
8	a novel	a long fiction story
9	a biography	the life story of a person
10	a directory	names listed in alphabetical order with addresses

Exercise 49

A

1 criminals 3 nuns 5 soldiers
2 monks 4 a ruler or a bishop

B

1 horses 3 rabbits 5 birds
2 eagles 4 bees

C

1 A studio is a workroom for an artist or a photographer.
OR
A studio is a place where sound recordings, films or broadcasts are made.
2 A mint is a place were coins are made.
3 An observatory is a building from which astronomers study the heavens.
4 A surgery is a room where a doctor or a dentist sees patients.
5 A library is a building or room containing a collection of books.

Exercise 50

A

1	custard:	milk, eggs, sugar
2	whisky:	fermented malt, barley or rye
3	chocolate:	cocoa
4	pasta:	flour paste
5	sausage:	minced and seasoned meat

B

1 cured ham
2 deer
3 vegetables, fruit
4 flesh
5 milk curd

ANSWERS

C
1 calf
2 grapes
3 Vitamins are essential for health and normal growth.
4 a tart without a cover
5 ingredients, directions

D

Freshwater fish	Sea-fish
pike	sole
roach	cod
trout	shark
perch	plaice
bream	haddock

E

1 root	2 cabbage	3 onion	4 root	5 edible, smell

Exercise 51

A
1 promenade: a place set aside for walking
2 motel: a hotel for motorists
3 safari: an expedition to see or to hunt big game
4 restaurant: a place where meals may be bought and eaten
5 itinerary: the details or route of a journey

B
1 ramble: a walk for pleasure
2 haversack: a canvas shoulder-bag for carrying food, clothing, etc.
3 fare: the charge made for a journey
4 excursion: a pleasure trip; an outing
5 destination: the place to which a person or thing is going

Exercise 52

A
1 regiment
2 to control and direct the course of an aircraft, ship or spacecraft
3 he/she controls an aircraft during a flight; he/she steers ships in and out of harbour
4 headquarters
5 rank
6 a person who has just joined the armed forces
7 captain, lieutenant-colonel
8 personal courage, especially in battle; bravery
9 for viewing objects above the surface or above eye-level
10 a sentry; a soldier on guard

ANSWERS

B
1 section of a fleet, regiment or air force
2 campaign
3 because he fires guns
4 rocket
5 caterpillar tracks
6 soldiers, warfare
7 soldier
8 a glider has no engine
9 a bomb for starting fires
10 it is in a suitable condition to sail on the sea

C
1	Capt.	Captain
2	Col.	Colonel
3	GI	enlisted soldier (USA)
4	HMS	Her/His Majesty's Ship
5	HQ	headquarters
6	Lieut.	Lieutenant
7	NATO	North Atlantic Treaty Organisation
8	POW	prisoner of war
9	RAF	Royal Air Force
10	Sgt.	Sergeant

Exercise 53

1 in the fifth and sixth centuries
2 for defence
3 small pieces of glass or stone
4 sword, dagger
5 the face
6 northern Germany
7 defensive walls, towers, trenches, etc.
8 a style having high and pointed arches
9 the later Stone Age
10 a book or paper written by hand

Exercise 54

1 violin
2 baritone, alto
3 musical notes
4 eight musical notes
5 five musicians, singers
6 at the beginning of a concert or opera
7 wood-wind
8 sorrowful
9 plates vibrate to give different notes when struck with a small hammer
10 singers, players

ANSWERS

Exercise 55

1	an obituary:	notice of someone's death
2	an encyclopedia:	information of general knowledge or of one particular subject
3	a (musical) score:	music showing vocal and instrumental parts
4	a script:	text of a film, play, radio or television programme
5	the Koran:	the Muslim scriptures
6	a log:	record of an aircraft's flight or ship's voyage
7	a manifesto:	what a ruler or group intends to do
8	an epilogue:	concluding, usually short, chapter of a book
9	an epitaph:	words inscribed on a tomb telling about the dead person
10	a will:	what a person wishes to be done with his/her property after death

Exercise 56

1 the return of the ball before it touches the ground
2 ninepins
3 ice sports or roller-skating
4 a toboggan
5 eleven
6 a beginner or learner
7 a disadvantage imposed for breaking a rule
8 a gymnast or acrobat
9 billiards and snooker
10 against

Exercise 57

A		B	
1	aisle	1	medal
2	throne	2	prey
3	main	3	stare
4	current	4	taut
5	Wine	5	Meet

Exercise 58

A		B	
1	comedy	1	rehearsal
2	playwright	2	tragedy
3	character	3	script
4	pantomime	4	stage
5	producer	5	drama

ANSWERS

Exercise 59

A

1 father's father
2 A draughtsman designs and draws plans.
3 war
4 yes
5 wandering

B

1 live alone
2 no
3 a hostel or college
4 A reporter collects news and information for a newspaper, radio or television.
5 to represent

Exercise 60

1 veil
2 made
3 feat
4 ancient Romans
5 later Stone Age
6 flour paste
7 anonymous; miscellaneous; reference; telephone; maximum
8 one
9 three
10 property or money

Exercise 61

1 a title: the name of a book, play, film or piece of music
                 OR
                 a word which shows a person's rank, position or profession
2 a narrative: a spoken or written account of what happened
3 a preface: an introduction to a book
4 a questionnaire: a list of questions to be answered
5 a prologue: an introduction to a play, poem, book or event

Exercise 62

| 1 antarctic | 3 antler | 5 disembark | 7 disobey | 9 enrich |
| 2 antique | 4 disband | 6 dishonest | 8 enrage | 10 encroach |

ANSWERS

Exercise 63

A The sentences should show the following meanings:

Word	Meaning
1 glorious	splendid; magnificent; famous; renowned
2 gaunt	thin; haggard; grim
3 enormous	very large; immense; huge
4 thrive	to grow vigorously; to prosper
5 pennant	a long, tapering flag

B

1 A beret is a flat, brimless woollen cap.
2 A helmet is a protective head cover worn by motor cyclists, soldiers, firemen, etc.
3 A veil is a piece of light material used to hide or protect the face.
4 A fez is a red, brimless hat with a black tassel, formerly worn by Turkish men.
5 A turban is a long cloth wound round the head, worn by Muslims, Hindus and Sikhs.

C

1 a pipe or duct to carry air, smoke or fumes; a ventilating shaft
2 the flow of water in a river
3 temperature
4 water or a canal
5 the flow of air, gas or liquid through a pipe

D

1 i.e.	that is (*L.* id est)
2 para.	paragraph
3 o.n.o.	or near offer
4 p.a.	yearly (*L.* per annum)
5 e.g.	for example (*L.* exempli gratia)

Exercise 64

A The explanations should include the following meanings:

subway	an underground passage
submarine	under water
subterranean	underground

B

1 quadruple   **2** subside   **3** novelty   **4** predict   **5** precise

C

1 in solitude
2 beginner, learner
3 spoils or destroys things
4 runs away or flees from something
5 works for an employer

Exercise 65

1 quick, skilful
2 false
3 yes
4 irritating
5 no
6 a climate that is neither very hot nor very cold
7 mountain ash
8 John Wesley
9 yes
10 hawk

Exercise 66

1 London
2 Greece
3 blowing air into a fire or an organ
4 stale, sour
5 A parallelogram is a four-sided shape with opposite sides parallel and equal.
6 a surgeon or a dentist
7 trick
8 omit
9 on rocks and trees
10 please turn over

Exercise 67

1 a choice; a right to choose
2 goose
3 yes
4 young trees
5 rat   red   rhyme   rice   road   rubber   rye
6 from the soft feathers of the eider duck
7 Switzerland
8 timid
9 facts
10 European Union

Exercise 68

1 flock	3 stable	5 rabbi	7 viper	9 hasp
2 goose	4 ladle	6 Thyme	8 tor	10 gaff

ANSWERS

Exercise 69
1 hibernate
2 recruit
3 journalist
4 tripod
5 spine
6 stubble
7 diary
8 tendon
9 electron
10 Vermilion

Exercise 70
1 on a ship
2 in a caravan
3 in barracks
4 in a monastery
5 in water, but can survive on land
6 in the sea
7 in a convent
8 near a river
9 in a vicarage
10 in a tree

Exercise 71
1 yes
2 endorse
3 death
4 on its own milk
5 misleading
6 fish
7 no
8 back
9 vocal cords
10 a soldier hired to fight for a foreign country

Exercise 72
1 swim, fly
2 the track and scent of an animal
3 a building which is neglected and needing repair
4 yes
5 yellow
6 sycamore
7 a maze
8 yes
9 a short, wise saying in general use
10 Justice of the Peace (J.P.)

Exercise 73
1 tailoress
2 grape
3 a small piece of cloth that is left over
4 things follow one another
5 no, it is beyond normal hearing range
6 word for word
7 story
8 cones
9 the strip of leather sewn between the sole and the upper part
10 to find and bring in game that has been shot

ANSWERS

Exercise 74

1 a rule or order
2 steep slope
3 hundredth
4 bells
5 outwards

6 the letters of another word
7 tar
8 plants
9 defeat
10 a delicate pattern of lines